# COLLINS CHECKBOOK

C000005452

# BRITISH BUTTERFLIES & MOTHS

 HarperCollins*Publishers*

HarperCollins*Publishers*
London Glasgow Sydney Auckland
Toronto Johannesburg
First published 1995

Compiled by Michael Chinery
© text, design and layout HarperCollins*Publishers* 1995
Based on an idea by Michael Solomon
Photographic consultants: David and Jean Hosking
The copyright in the photographs belongs to the following photographers
from the Frank Lane Picture Agency:
T Benton 16; R Bird 39, 59, 63, 226; B Borrell 176; H D Brandl 64, 138; S C
Brown 44; M Chinery 73, 80, 87, 98, 129, 142, 146, 160, 163, 167, 182, 194,
196, 199, 205, 214, 217, 218, 228; H Clark 43, 53, 113, 136; E A Dean 75,
101, 155, 206; G Dickson 169, 207, 215; M Evans 67, 69, 83, 84, 96, 104, 106,
110, 118, 120, 157, 166, 184, 186, 187, 188, 192, 195, 201, 209, 213, 224; A R
Hamblin 225; M Hollings 28; E & D Hosking 1, 13, 30, 38, 42, 70, 91, 135, 139,
148, 179; J Hutchings 178; G E Hyde 2, 26, 31, 33 (cover), 35, 50, 57, 68, 71,
78, 82, 86, 88, 93, 94, 95 (back cover), 97, 99, 103, 105, 107, 109, 111, 112,
117, 122, 124, 125, 126, 130, 133, 137, 143, 152, 154, 156, 159, 161, 162, 164,
165, 168, 170, 171, 175, 177, 180, 185, 189, 191, 197, 198, 202, 203, 204, 208,
211, 219, 221, 222, 223; P Jerrold 81, 100, 181, 190, 193; D Jones 18; F Merlet
3, 48; C Mullen 77; C Newton 19, 41, 55, 60; G Perrone/Panda 72;
Premaphotos 90; P Reynolds 174; A J Roberts 172; W Rohdich p. 4; I Rose
74, 92, 102, 121, 123, 127; M Rose 147; Silvestris 17, 145; J Swale 183; M J
Thomas 56; R Tidman 144, 150; J Tinning 15, 49, 54, 140; J Trinder 200; J
Watkins 9; L West 66; A Wharton 5, 7, 12, 22, 46, 52, 58, 65, 79, 85, 89, 108,
116, 128, 131, 134, 149, 151, 153, 158, 173, 210, 212, 216, 220; R Wilmshurst
4, 6, 8, 10, 11, 14, 20, 21, 23, 24, 25, 27, 29, 32, 34, 36, 37, 40, 45, 47, 51, 61,
62, 76, 114; M B Withers 115, 119, 132, 141, 227

ISBN 000 220020 1

Colour reproduction by Colourscan, Singapore
Printed and bound in Italy by Arnoldo Mondadori Editore SpA

# ABOUT THIS BOOK

Butterflies and moths are among the most colourful and conspicuous of our insects and this book has been designed for you to record your observations of more than 200 kinds or species found in the British Isles. Most of them are quite common, but a few eye-catching rarities are also included. All our resident butterflies are pictured, together with a number of regular and occasional summer visitors. Over 2000 kinds of moths inhabit the British Isles, but most of these are very small and the species chosen for this book are mainly the larger and more striking ones. These can usually be identified simply from their wing patterns. English and scientific names are given for each species. Closely-related species have similar scientific names and often look alike. Those species marked Ⓔ are endangered. The measurements given are normal averages for the length of the forewing.

The panels are for you to fill in as and when you find each species. **Date** and **locality** will serve as useful reminders of when and where to find a species again, for most species fly only at certain seasons. **Habitat** is the insect's surroundings - woodland clearing, downland, garden, and so on. Record **numbers**, in the box labelled **No.**, in a simple way - whether there are plenty of insects scattered all over the place, just a few, or only single individuals in the area concerned. Recording **activity** will reveal a good deal about the insects' habits: are they resting, feeding, flying actively, mating, or laying eggs? What flowers are they visiting or laying eggs on? Many butterflies and moths have distinct times for rest and activity, so it is also useful to record the **time** of day and the **weather**. Ticking the **all time record** box each time you see a species will give you some idea how common the insects are.

# THE BUTTERFLY BODY

Butterflies and moths belong to the large group of insects called the Lepidoptera. This name means 'scale wings', and if you look at the wings with a lens you will see that they are clothed with minute **scales**, overlapping each other like tiles on a roof. It is these scales that give the wings their beautiful colours and patterns.

Adult butterflies and moths take liquid food, which they suck up through a hair-like tube called the **proboscis**. Rolled up under the head when not in use, and uncoiled when the insect is about to feed, it is longer than the body in some species. It is very easy to see the proboscis in action when butterflies are feeding at flowers. Nectar is the main food of both butterflies and moths, but many woodland butterflies feed on honeydew - the sugary secretion of aphids. Some even enjoy sipping the putrid juices of decaying animals, and it is also common to see butterflies drinking from puddles and wet ground. Some moths, including the Emperor (136), have no proboscis and do not feed in the adult state. All their feeding and growing takes place in the caterpillar stage (see Life Cycles) and their adult life is devoted entirely to finding mates and laying eggs.

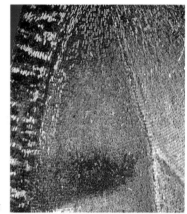

*Close-up of the scales on a butterfly's wing*

# BUTTERFLY OR MOTH?

No single feature will separate all butterflies from all moths, but as far as our British species are concerned it is quite easy to separate the two groups by looking at the feelers or antennae on their heads. All our butterflies have little knobs at the ends of their antennae. Moth antennae are mostly hair-like or feathery and, although some of them gradually get thicker towards the tip, they never have distinct knobs at the end.

Resting attitudes also help to distinguish butterflies from moths. Almost all butterflies rest at night and in dull weather with their wings closed vertically over their bodies and only the undersides visible. Most moths rest with their wings flat or folded roof-like over the body so that only the uppersides are visible, although some thorn moths (110-112) rest with their wings in the butterfly position. The undersides of butterfly wings usually blend in well with the surroundings when the insects are at rest, making them quite difficult to spot, but it is usually the uppersides of moths that are camouflaged, concealing the insects as they rest on tree trunks and vegetation by day.

It is often said that butterflies are active by day and moths are active by night, but this is not entirely true: there are many day-flying moths and some of them are as brightly coloured as any butterfly. The burnet moths (76-78) are good examples.

Butterfly: clubbed

Skipper butterfly: hooked club

Emperor Moth: feathered

Geometer Moth: hair-like

Shapes of antennae

# LIFE CYCLES

All butterflies and moths start life as eggs. Tiny caterpillars leave the eggs and begin a life of almost continuous feeding, munching their way through the surrounding leaves. Most species are quite fussy about their food and the females are careful to lay their eggs on the right plants. Feeding goes on for several weeks, with a few short breaks during which the caterpillars change their skins. When a caterpillar reaches its full size - anything from about 1cm to 13cm in British species - it prepares to turn into a pupa or chrysalis. Moth caterpillars either burrow into the ground, where each makes a little chamber for itself, or else surround themselves with silken cocoons. Some butterfly caterpillars make flimsy cocoons on the ground, but most of them simply attach themselves to twigs or leaves with silken threads. When preparations are complete the caterpillar shrugs off its skin to reveal the chrysalis. Although some-

times described as a resting stage, there is great activity inside it as the caterpillar's body is broken down and re-built into that of the adult butterfly or moth. This can take as little as ten days, although many species actually pass the winter in the chrysalis stage. Eventually, the chrysalis skin splits and the adult insect struggles out - soft and crumpled at first, but its wings soon expand and dry and then it can fly away.

# WHAT YOU NEED

Very little is necessary in the way of equipment for spotting butterflies and moths. Most of the species pictured in this book can be recognised without catching them - as long as they sit still for a while - but it is sometimes necessary to capture the occasional specimen to take a closer look, and for this you need a net. The net bag should be at least 30cm across and 50cm deep - large enough for you to get your hands into it and deep enough to trap the insect securely inside. Soft black nylon netting is the best material. Having caught an insect, carefully manipulate it into a clear plastic box or a small jar so that you can examine it. If it refuses to sit still, simply put the container in the dark for a few minutes. Release the insect as soon as you have examined it.

It is possible to buy moth traps, which attract night-flying moths with powerful lights and trap them harmlessly until you can examine them in the morning, but you can attract plenty of moths simply by shining a strong light on to a white sheet in the garden.

A pocket lens or hand lens is always useful for examining some of the smaller species that you catch. One with a magnification of about x10 should be adequate for picking out the finer details of the wings. Try to find a lens that can be threaded on a cord and carried around your neck: you will be less likely to lose it then! Binoculars can be useful for watching butterflies high in the trees or in other inaccessible places.

# WHERE TO GO

Some of our butterflies, such as Peacock and Brimstone, have no fixed homes. You can find them wherever there are good supplies of nectar. At least twelve species regularly visit gardens, including those in the middle of towns, and town parks with lots of flowers are excellent places to watch these butterflies. You might also see the Hummingbird Hawkmoth and other day-flying moths.

Other butterfly species are much less mobile, rarely going far from where they grew up. You need to know their preferred habitats and food-plants if you want to find these butterflies. Find their food-plants and you might find their caterpillars as well. Most of our fritillaries like open woodlands, especially coppiced woodlands and those with flowery rides. Some of the browns also like woodland rides, but others prefer open grassland, where they mingle with the blues and skippers. Ancient woodlands and the chalk and limestone hills of southern England are among the best places in which to look for butterflies. The south of Britain has more species than the north because it is warmer.

A good way of finding night-flying moths is to look around street-lamps. The lights attract the moths and it is not difficult to catch them with a long-handled net. You can also find moths resting on fences and tree trunks early in the morning. When you 'get your eye in' you'll be surprised at how many you can find - and you'll appreciate how well camouflaged they are. The greatest numbers can usually found near the street-lamps that attracted them during the night.

# A Code for Naturalists

Our wildlife is a precious asset, so do nothing to endanger it while you are looking for or watching butterflies and moths. The welfare and safety of the insects is far more important than getting a good view or a good photograph. Extensive trampling around bushes or other plants while trying to photograph butterflies can destroy flowers that other people - and insects - would enjoy. It can also draw unwelcome attention to the feeding sites of the butterflies and caterpillars and actually expose the insects to danger.

It is rarely necessary to catch butterflies and moths for identification, and you can certainly enjoy them without catching them. Follow the advice of Harold Oldroyd, a well-known entomologist, who wrote: '...do not be in a hurry to catch and kill insects, but spend as much time as you can watching them going about their daily life'. And then leave them for others to enjoy.

Do as little damage to the environment as is possible, leaving the area as you found it and giving no-one cause to regret your visit.

## The Country Code

Always obey the Country Code when in the countryside:

1. Leave no litter
2. Fasten all gates
3. Avoid damaging fences, hedges, and walls
4. Guard against all risk of fire
5. Keep dogs under control
6. Keep to paths across farmland
7. Safeguard all water supplies
8. Protect all forms of wildlife
9. Go carefully on country roads
10. Respect the life of the countryside

## 1 CHEQUERED SKIPPER *Carterocephalus palaemon*

R

14mm. Extinct in England but not uncommon in parts of western Scotland.

| Date & Time | No. |
| | |

**Weather**

**Locality**

**Habitat**

All Time Record

| | | | | | | | | | |

**Activity**

## 2 SMALL SKIPPER *Thymelicus sylvestris* Echo

R

15mm. Male in typical basking position. Female lacks black bar on forewing.

| Date & Time | No. |
| | |

**Weather**

**Locality**

**Habitat**

All Time Record

| | | | | | | | | | |

**Activity**

3 ESSEX SKIPPER *Thymelicus lineola* Echo

14mm. Very like Small Skipper but tips of antennae are black.

| Date & Time | No. |
|---|---|
| | |

Weather

Locality

Habitat

All Time Record

| | | | | | | | | | |
|---|---|---|---|---|---|---|---|---|---|

Activity

R

4 LULWORTH SKIPPER *Thymelicus acteon*

13mm. In typical basking position of most skippers, with forewings raised.

| Date & Time | No. |
|---|---|
| | |

Weather

Locality

Habitat

All Time Record

| | | | | | | | | | |
|---|---|---|---|---|---|---|---|---|---|

Activity

R

## 5 LARGE SKIPPER *Ochlodes venatus*

R

16mm. Mating pair. Upperside is rich brown with golden patches.

**Date & Time**

**No.**

**Weather**

**Locality**

**Habitat**

All Time Record

**Activity**

## 6 SILVER-SPOTTED SKIPPER E *Hesperia comma*

R

15mm. Silver spots distinguish it from other skippers. Very rare.

**Date & Time**

**No.**

**Weather**

**Locality**

**Habitat**

All Time Record

**Activity**

## 7 DINGY SKIPPER *Erynnis tages*

14mm. Basks with wings wide open. The only skipper in Ireland.

**All Time Record**

| | | | | | | | | | |
|---|---|---|---|---|---|---|---|---|---|
| | | | | | | | | | |

| R |
|---|

**Date & Time**

| | No. |
|---|---|

**Weather**

**Locality**

**Habitat**

**Activity**

## 8 GRIZZLED SKIPPER *Pyrgus malvae*

12mm. Basks with wings wide open, often on the ground.

**All Time Record**

| | | | | | | | | | |
|---|---|---|---|---|---|---|---|---|---|
| | | | | | | | | | |

| R |
|---|

**Date & Time**

| | No. |
|---|---|

**Weather**

**Locality**

**Habitat**

**Activity**

## 9 SWALLOWTAIL (E) *Papilio machaon*

R

45mm. An unmistakable butterfly, with tail-like projections on the hind wing.

**Date & Time**

**No.**

**Weather**

**Locality**

**Habitat**

**All Time Record**

**Activity**

## 10 LARGE WHITE *Pieris brassicae* Echo.

R

35mm. Female. Male lacks black spots. A cabbage pest.

**Date & Time**

**No.**

**Weather**

**Locality**

**Habitat**

**All Time Record**

**Activity**

## 11 SMALL WHITE *Pieris rapae* Echo

25mm. Female. Male has only one black spot or none at all. A cabbage pest.

| | R |
|---|---|

**Date & Time** — No.

**Weather**

**Locality**

**Habitat**

**Activity**

All Time Record

## 12 GREEN-VEINED WHITE *Pieris napi*

25mm. Mating pair. Not a cabbage pest.

| | R |
|---|---|

**Date & Time** — No.

**Weather**

**Locality**

**Habitat**

**Activity**

All Time Record

## 13 BATH WHITE *Pontia daplidice*

S

24mm. A rare visitor. Wing-tips are more pointed than female Orange-tip.

**Date & Time**

**No.**

**Weather**

**Locality**

**Habitat**

All Time Record

**Activity**

## 14 ORANGE-TIP *Anthocharis cardamines* Echo

R

24mm. Male. Female has no orange.

**Date & Time**

**No.**

**Weather**

**Locality**

**Habitat**

All Time Record

**Activity**

## 15 CLOUDED YELLOW *Colias crocea*

27mm. Upperside deep yellow with black edges. Most common in south.

**All Time Record**

| | | | | | | | | | | |
|--|--|--|--|--|--|--|--|--|--|--|

S

**Date & Time**

**No.**

**Weather**

**Locality**

**Habitat**

**Activity**

## 16 BERGER'S CLOUDED YELLOW *Colias australis*

27mm. Upperside lemon yellow (male) or white (female) with black borders.

**All Time Record**

| | | | | | | | | | | |
|--|--|--|--|--|--|--|--|--|--|--|

S

**Date & Time**

**No.**

**Weather**

**Locality**

**Habitat**

**Activity**

## 17 PALE CLOUDED YELLOW *Colias hyale*

S

25mm. Very like Berger's Clouded Yellow but a little paler.

**Date & Time**

No.

**Weather**

**Locality**

**Habitat**

**All Time Record**

**Activity**

## 18 BRIMSTONE *Gonepteryx rhamni*

R

30mm. Mating pair. Male has brilliant yellow upperside, female greenish white.

**Date & Time**

No.

**Weather**

**Locality**

**Habitat**

**All Time Record**

**Activity**

## 19 WOOD WHITE *Leptidea sinapis*

R

21mm. Courting pair. Black or grey wing-tips on upperside. Very delicate.

**All Time Record**

| | | | | | | | | | | | |
|---|---|---|---|---|---|---|---|---|---|---|---|

| Date & Time | No. |
|---|---|
| | |

**Weather**

**Locality**

**Habitat**

**Activity**

## 20 GREEN HAIRSTREAK *Callophrys rubi*

R

15mm. Upperside is plain brown, but always rests with wings closed.

**All Time Record**

| | | | | | | | | | | | |
|---|---|---|---|---|---|---|---|---|---|---|---|

| Date & Time | No. |
|---|---|
| | |

**Weather**

**Locality**

**Habitat**

**Activity**

## 21 PURPLE HAIRSTREAK *Quercusia quercus*

R

14mm. Female. Male has purple sheen over all wings. Underside is grey.

**Date & Time**

**No.**

**Weather**

**Locality**

**Habitat**

All Time Record

**Activity**

## 22 BROWN HAIRSTREAK *Thecla betulae*

R

18mm. Upperside is brown with red tails and female has orange patch on forewing.

**Date & Time**

**No.**

**Weather**

**Locality**

**Habitat**

All Time Record

**Activity**

**23 WHITE-LETTER HAIRSTREAK** *Strymonidia w-album*  R

15mm. White streak on underside forms a
W. Upperside, hidden at rest, is brown.

Date & Time

No.

Weather

Locality

Habitat

All Time Record

Activity

---

**24 BLACK HAIRSTREAK** *Strymonidia pruni*  R

16mm. Upperside, never seen at rest, is
dark brown with orange margins.

Date & Time

No.

Weather

Locality

Habitat

All Time Record

Activity

## 25 SMALL COPPER *Lycaena phlaeas*

15mm. Black spots vary in size. Likes to bask on ground.

All Time Record

| | | | | | | | | | | | |
|---|---|---|---|---|---|---|---|---|---|---|---|

R

| Date & Time | No. |
|---|---|
| | |

Weather

Locality

Habitat

Activity

## 26 LONG-TAILED BLUE *Lampides boeticus*

16mm. Male. Female has blackish hind wing and wide black margins on forewing.

All Time Record

| | | | | | | | | | | | |
|---|---|---|---|---|---|---|---|---|---|---|---|

S

| Date & Time | No. |
|---|---|
| | |

Weather

Locality

Habitat

Activity

**27 SMALL BLUE** *Cupido minimus*      R

12mm. Mating pair. Upperside is brown with a dusting of blue scales in male.

**All Time Record**

| | | | | | | | | | | |
|---|---|---|---|---|---|---|---|---|---|---|

Date & Time      No.

Weather

Locality

Habitat

Activity

**28 SILVER-STUDDED BLUE** *Plebejus argus*      R

14mm. Male. Female is brown. Underside has silvery dots near edge of hind wing.

**All Time Record**

| | | | | | | | | | | |
|---|---|---|---|---|---|---|---|---|---|---|

Date & Time      No.

Weather

Locality

Habitat

Activity

## 29 BROWN ARGUS  *Aricia agestis*

14mm. Underside is pale brown with black dots and orange marginal spots.

R

**Date & Time**

**No.**

**Weather**

**Locality**

**Habitat**

**All Time Record**

**Activity**

## 30 NORTHERN BROWN ARGUS  *Aricia artaxerxes*

12mm. Very like Brown Argus, but usually with white spot on forewing.

R

**Date & Time**

**No.**

**Weather**

**Locality**

**Habitat**

**All Time Record**

**Activity**

## 31 COMMON BLUE *Polyommatus icarus*

R

17mm. Male. Female generally brown with orange spots and scattered blue scales.

**Date & Time**

**No.**

**Weather**

**Locality**

**Habitat**

**All Time Record**

**Activity**

## 32 CHALKHILL BLUE *Lysandra coridon*

R

18mm. Male. Female is brown with some pale blue scales near the body.

**Date & Time**

**No.**

**Weather**

**Locality**

**Habitat**

**All Time Record**

**Activity**

## 33 ADONIS BLUE *Lysandra bellargus* [R]

17mm. Male. Female very like Chalkhill Blue but often a little darker.

| Date & Time | No. |
| | |

Weather

Locality

Habitat

All Time Record

| | | | | | | | | | | | | |

Activity

## 34 HOLLY BLUE *Celastrina argiolus* [R]

17mm. Upperside is clear blue, with broad black borders in female.

| Date & Time | No. |
| | |

Weather

Locality

Habitat

All Time Record

| | | | | | | | | | | | | |

Activity

## 35 LARGE BLUE (E) *Maculinea arion*

20mm. Male. Female has broader margins.
Re-established after becoming extinct.

R

| Date & Time | No. |
| --- | --- |
|  |  |

Weather

Locality

Habitat

All Time Record

Activity

## 36 DUKE OF BURGUNDY *Hamearis lucina*

15mm. Like Chequered Skipper but orange
spots at margins have black centres.

R

| Date & Time | No. |
| --- | --- |
|  |  |

Weather

Locality

Habitat

All Time Record

Activity

## 37 WHITE ADMIRAL *Limenitis camilla* | R |

30mm. Underside rusty brown and white. Glides rapidly around trees and bushes.

**Date & Time** | **No.**

**Weather**

**Locality**

**Habitat**

**All Time Record**

**Activity**

## 38 PURPLE EMPEROR *Apatura iris* | R |

40mm. Male. Female lacks purple. Keeps mainly to tree tops.

**Date & Time** | **No.**

**Weather**

**Locality**

**Habitat**

**All Time Record**

**Activity**

## 39 RED ADMIRAL *Vanessa atalanta*

31mm. A strong-flying, regular summer visitor. Very fond of ripe fruit.

**All Time Record**

| | | | | | | | | | |
|---|---|---|---|---|---|---|---|---|---|

S

**Date & Time**

**No.**

**Weather**

**Locality**

**Habitat**

**Activity**

## 40 PAINTED LADY *Cynthia cardui*

28mm. A regular visitor, but generally less common than Red Admiral.

**All Time Record**

| | | | | | | | | | |
|---|---|---|---|---|---|---|---|---|---|

S

**Date & Time**

**No.**

**Weather**

**Locality**

**Habitat**

**Activity**

## 41 SMALL TORTOISESHELL *Aglais urticae*

25mm. Hibernates as adult and one of the first butterflies to appear in spring.

R

**Date & Time**

**No.**

**Weather**

**Locality**

**Habitat**

**All Time Record**

**Activity**

## 42 LARGE TORTOISESHELL Ⓔ *Nymphalis polychloros*

32mm. Less black on hind wing than Small Tortoiseshell. May be extinct in Britain.

R

**Date & Time**

**No.**

**Weather**

**Locality**

**Habitat**

**All Time Record**

**Activity**

43 CAMBERWELL BEAUTY *Nymphalis antiopa*

33mm. An unmistakable butterfly, rarely seen in Britain.

All Time Record

| S |

Date & Time

No.

Weather

Locality

Habitat

Activity

44 PEACOCK *Inachis io*

32mm. An unmistakable insect. Underside almost black. Hibernates as an adult.

All Time Record

| R |

Date & Time

No.

Weather

Locality

Habitat

Activity

## 45 COMMA *Polygonia c-album*

27mm. Has a white comma-shaped mark on underside. Often darker in autumn.

R

**Date & Time**

**No.**

**Weather**

**Locality**

**Habitat**

All Time Record

**Activity**

## 46 SMALL PEARL-BORDERED FRITILLARY *Clossiana selene*

21mm. Underside of hind wing has border of pearly spots. Mainly in upland areas.

R

**Date & Time**

**No.**

**Weather**

**Locality**

**Habitat**

All Time Record

**Activity**

## 47 PEARL-BORDERED FRITILLARY *Clossiana euphrosyne* | R |

23mm. Underside of hind wing has pearly border and a large central silver spot.

**Date & Time** | **No.**

**Weather**

**Locality**

**Habitat**

**All Time Record**

**Activity**

## 48 QUEEN OF SPAIN FRITILLARY *Issoria lathonia* | S |

22mm. Very large silver spots on underside of hind wing. A rare visitor.

**Date & Time** | **No.**

**Weather**

**Locality**

**Habitat**

**All Time Record**

**Activity**

## 49 HIGH BROWN FRITILLARY **E** *Fabriciana adippe*

R

31mm. One of our rarest butterflies.
Underside has silver and rusty spots.

**All Time Record**

**Date & Time**

No.

**Weather**

**Locality**

**Habitat**

**Activity**

## 50 DARK GREEN FRITILLARY *Mesoacidalia aglaja*

R

30mm. Underside of hind wing green with
silver spots but no rusty spots.

**All Time Record**

**Date & Time**

No.

**Weather**

**Locality**

**Habitat**

**Activity**

## 51 SILVER-WASHED FRITILLARY  *Argynnis paphia*

35mm. Male. Female has no dark streaks.
Underside is green with silver streaks.

R

| Date & Time | No. |
|---|---|
|  |  |

Weather

Locality

Habitat

All Time Record

| | | | | | | | | | |
|---|---|---|---|---|---|---|---|---|---|

Activity

## 52 MARSH FRITILLARY  *Eurodryas aurinia*

20mm. Spots vary, but always an arc of
black dots on both sides of hind wing.

R

| Date & Time | No. |
|---|---|
|  |  |

Weather

Locality

Habitat

All Time Record

| | | | | | | | | | |
|---|---|---|---|---|---|---|---|---|---|

Activity

## 53 GLANVILLE FRITILLARY *Melitaea cinxia*

22mm. Underside of hind wing cream with orange bands. Confined to Isle of Wight.

R

**Date & Time**

**No.**

**Weather**

**Locality**

**Habitat**

**All Time Record**

**Activity**

## 54 HEATH FRITILLARY E *Mellicta athalia*

21mm. Like Glanville Fritillary but no arc of black dots in the hind wing.

R

**Date & Time**

**No.**

**Weather**

**Locality**

**Habitat**

**All Time Record**

**Activity**

## 55 SPECKLED WOOD *Pararge aegeria*

R

23mm. An unmistakable insect often seen basking in patches of sunlight in woods.

| Date & Time | No. |
|---|---|
| | |

Weather

Locality

Habitat

All Time Record

Activity

## 56 WALL *Lasiommata megera*

R

25mm. Likes to bask on ground or rocks. Eye-spots distinguish it from fritillaries.

| Date & Time | No. |
|---|---|
| | |

Weather

Locality

Habitat

All Time Record

Activity

## 57 MOUNTAIN RINGLET *Erebia epiphron*

19mm. Upperside is velvety brown with orange patches. A northern species.

**All Time Record**

| | | | | | | | | | |
|---|---|---|---|---|---|---|---|---|---|
| | | | | | | | | | |

R

Date & Time

No.

Weather

Locality

Habitat

Activity

## 58 SCOTCH ARGUS *Erebia aethiops*

25mm. Upperside similar but with orange band on hind wing as well. Northern.

**All Time Record**

| | | | | | | | | | |
|---|---|---|---|---|---|---|---|---|---|
| | | | | | | | | | |

R

Date & Time

No.

Weather

Locality

Habitat

Activity

## 59 MARBLED WHITE *Melanargia galathea* R

26mm. Eye-spots and black-and-white pattern make this species unmistakable.

**Date & Time** | **No.**

**Weather**

**Locality**

**Habitat**

**All Time Record**

**Activity**

## 60 GRAYLING *Hipparchia semele* R

25mm. Upperside, never seen at rest, is brown with golden patches.

**Date & Time** | **No.**

**Weather**

**Locality**

**Habitat**

**All Time Record**

**Activity**

## 61 GATEKEEPER *Pyronia tithonus*

20mm. Male. Female lacks brown streak in forewing. Also called Hedge Brown.

**R**

Date & Time

No.

Weather

Locality

Habitat

All Time Record

Activity

## 62 MEADOW BROWN *Maniola jurtina*

25mm. Female. Male has much less orange and a dark streak in forewing.

**R**

Date & Time

No.

Weather

Locality

Habitat

All Time Record

Activity

## 63 RINGLET *Aphantopus hyperantus*

24mm. Eye-spots may be obscure.
Underside is paler with prominent rings.

All Time Record

Date & Time

No.

Weather

Locality

Habitat

Activity

## 64 SMALL HEATH *Coenonympha pamphilus*

18mm. Upperside, never seen at rest, is
orange-brown with narrow grey margins.

All Time Record

Date & Time

No.

Weather

Locality

Habitat

Activity

## 65 LARGE HEATH *Coenonympha tullia*

20mm. Upperside, never seen at rest, is orange with a dusting of grey scales.

**R**

Date & Time

No.

Weather

Locality

Habitat

All Time Record

Activity

## 66 MONARCH *Danaus plexippus*

47mm. An unmistakable, but very infrequent visitor.

**S**

Date & Time

No.

Weather

Locality

Habitat

All Time Record

Activity

**67** GHOST SWIFT *Hepialus humuli*

22mm. Male. Female is yellowish. Male dances up and down like a ghost at dusk.

All Time Record

R

Date & Time

No.

Weather

Locality

Habitat

Activity

**68** COMMON SWIFT *Hepialus lupulinus*

18mm. Very variable, often with conspicuous white markings.

All Time Record

R

Date & Time

No.

Weather

Locality

Habitat

Activity

**69 GOLD SWIFT** *Hepialus hecta*

15mm. Male. Female is paler with less distinct markings.

R

Date & Time

No.

Weather

Locality

Habitat

All Time Record

Activity

**70** *Nemophora degeerella*

10mm. Male, with longest antennae of any British moth. Female antennae shorter.

R

Date & Time

No.

Weather

Locality

Habitat

All Time Record

Activity

71 *Adela reaumurella*

9mm. Male. Dances in swarms over bushes in spring. Female antennae shorter.

R

Date & Time

No.

Weather

Locality

Habitat

All Time Record

Activity

72 GOAT MOTH *Cossus cossus*

45mm. Caterpillar tunnels in tree trunks and smells like goats.

R

Date & Time

No.

Weather

Locality

Habitat

All Time Record

Activity

**73 LEOPARD MOTH** *Zeuzera pyrina*

34mm. Caterpillar can be a pest by tunnelling in the trunks of fruit trees.

R

Date & Time

No.

Weather

Locality

Habitat

All Time Record

Activity

**74 GREEN OAK TORTRIX** *Tortrix viridana*

9mm. Caterpillars often drop on silken threads from oak branches.

R

Date & Time

No.

Weather

Locality

Habitat

All Time Record

Activity

## 75 LUNAR HORNET CLEARWING *Sphecia bembeciformis* [R]

18mm. A day-flying moth, well protected by its resemblance to a hornet.

**Date & Time**

**No.**

**Weather**

**Locality**

**Habitat**

**All Time Record**

**Activity**

## 76 6-SPOT BURNET *Zygaena filipendulae* [R]

18mm. Day-flying, but rather sluggish like all burnets.

**Date & Time**

**No.**

**Weather**

**Locality**

**Habitat**

**All Time Record**

**Activity**

**77 5-SPOT BURNET** *Zygaena trifolii*

18mm. Mating pair, on papery cocoon typical of burnets. Day-flying.

All Time Record

| | | | | | | | | | | |
|---|---|---|---|---|---|---|---|---|---|---|

R

Date & Time

No.

Weather

Locality

Habitat

Activity

**78 TRANSPARENT BURNET** *Zygaena purpuralis*

16mm. Thinly scaled and often with hardly any red at all. Day-flying.

All Time Record

| | | | | | | | | | | |
|---|---|---|---|---|---|---|---|---|---|---|

R

Date & Time

No.

Weather

Locality

Habitat

Activity

## 79 FORESTER *Adscita statices*

12mm. Day-flying, but rather sluggish. One of several similar species.

R

| Date & Time | No. |
|---|---|
|  |  |

Weather

Locality

Habitat

All Time Record

| | | | | | | | | | | |
|---|---|---|---|---|---|---|---|---|---|---|

Activity

## 80 WHITE PLUME *Pterophorus pentadactylus*

12mm. Feathery wings are wrapped around each other at rest, as pictured here.

R

| Date & Time | No. |
|---|---|
|  |  |

Weather

Locality

Habitat

All Time Record

| | | | | | | | | | | |
|---|---|---|---|---|---|---|---|---|---|---|

Activity

## 81 SMALL MAGPIE *Eurrhypara hortulata*

12mm. Often abundant in nettle beds, where caterpillars feed.

R

**Date & Time**

**No.**

**Weather**

**Locality**

**Habitat**

All Time Record

**Activity**

## 82 MOTHER-OF-PEARL *Pleuroptya ruralis*

13mm. Common in nettle beds and often comes to lighted windows at night.

R

**Date & Time**

**No.**

**Weather**

**Locality**

**Habitat**

All Time Record

**Activity**

**83 MEAL MOTH** *Pyralis farinalis*

R

12mm. Often in houses. Caterpillar feeds on flour and other cereal products.

Date & Time

No.

Weather

Locality

Habitat

All Time Record

Activity

**84 GOLD FRINGE** *Hypsopygia costalis*

R

8mm. Often rests with wings wide open and tail up-turned.

Date & Time

No.

Weather

Locality

Habitat

All Time Record

Activity

**85** LARGE EMERALD *Geometra papilionaria*

30mm. The green fades with age and may disappear altogether after death.

All Time Record

| | | | | | | | | |
|---|---|---|---|---|---|---|---|---|

R

| Date & Time | No. |
|---|---|
| | |

Weather

Locality

Habitat

Activity

---

**86** COMMON EMERALD *Hemithea aestivaria*

15mm. Chequered margins. Hind wing has a prominent point.

All Time Record

| | | | | | | | | |
|---|---|---|---|---|---|---|---|---|

R

| Date & Time | No. |
|---|---|
| | |

Weather

Locality

Habitat

Activity

**87 SMALL EMERALD** *Hemistola chrysoprasaria*

12mm. The delicate green fades with age and older specimens are often white.

R

Date & Time

No.

Weather

Locality

Habitat

All Time Record

Activity

**88 LIGHT EMERALD** *Campaea margaritata*

25mm. Central band may be much paler. Not closely related to other emeralds.

R

Date & Time

No.

Weather

Locality

Habitat

All Time Record

Activity

## 89 BLOODVEIN  *Timandra griseata*

15mm. Wing colour varies from white to deep pink, but 'vein' is always obvious.

**All Time Record**

| R |
| --- |

**Date & Time**

**No.**

**Weather**

**Locality**

**Habitat**

**Activity**

## 90 COMMON CARPET  *Epirrhoe alternata*

14mm. Both white bands enclose a thin, wavy black line.

**All Time Record**

| R |
| --- |

**Date & Time**

**No.**

**Weather**

**Locality**

**Habitat**

**Activity**

## 91 Garden Carpet *Xanthorrhoe fluctuata*

R

14mm. Very dark 'shoulders'. Central black patch may extend across wing.

| Date & Time | No. |
| --- | --- |
| | |

Weather

Locality

Habitat

All Time Record

Activity

## 92 Yellow Shell *Camptogramma bilineata*

R

14mm. Wavy bands are much thinner in some specimens.

| Date & Time | No. |
| --- | --- |
| | |

Weather

Locality

Habitat

All Time Record

Activity

## 93 NORTHERN SPINACH *Eulithis populata*

17mm. Often rests with wings well away from body, like Barred Straw.

**All Time Record**

| R |

**Date & Time**

**No.**

**Weather**

**Locality**

**Habitat**

**Activity**

## 94 BARRED STRAW *Eulithis pyraliata*

17mm. Very like Spinach Moth, but the latter has chequered margins.

**All Time Record**

| R |

**Date & Time**

**No.**

**Weather**

**Locality**

**Habitat**

**Activity**

95 BARRED YELLOW *Cidaria fulvata*

14mm. Often rests with abdomen held vertically.

All Time Record

| | | | | | | | | | | |
|---|---|---|---|---|---|---|---|---|---|---|

R

Date & Time · No.

Weather

Locality

Habitat

Activity

96 GREEN CARPET *Colostygia pectinataria*

14mm. The green colour fades with age, and especially after death.

All Time Record

| | | | | | | | | | | |
|---|---|---|---|---|---|---|---|---|---|---|

R

Date & Time No.

Weather

Locality

Habitat

Activity

**97 PRETTY CHALK CARPET** *Melanthia procellata*

20mm. The white blotch in the dark outer margin separates this from other carpets.

R

Date & Time

No.

Weather

Locality

Habitat

All Time Record

Activity

**98 SMALL WAVED UMBER** *Horisme vitalbata*

17mm. Common, but hard to see at rest on tree trunks because of superb camouflage.

R

Date & Time

No.

Weather

Locality

Habitat

All Time Record

Activity

## 99 WINTER MOTH *Operophtera brumata*

15mm. Male, often seen on window panes in mid-winter. Female is wingless.

R

**Date & Time**

**No.**

**Weather**

**Locality**

**Habitat**

**All Time Record**

**Activity**

## 100 LIME-SPECK PUG *Eupithecia centaureata*

11mm. The resting position, with wings far from the body, is typical of pugs.

R

**Date & Time**

**No.**

**Weather**

**Locality**

**Habitat**

**All Time Record**

**Activity**

## 101 NETTED PUG *Eupithecia venosata*

11mm. Wings may be browner with more distinct white lines.

R

**Date & Time**

No.

**Weather**

**Locality**

**Habitat**

All Time Record

**Activity**

## 102 TREBLE BAR *Aplocera plagiata*

20mm. Innermost (shortest) of three bars is not sharply toothed.

R

**Date & Time**

No.

**Weather**

**Locality**

**Habitat**

All Time Record

**Activity**

## 103 Magpie Moth *Abraxas grossulariata*

22mm. Common in gardens. Caterpillar attacks currant and gooseberry bushes.

R

| Date & Time | No. |
|---|---|
| | |

Weather

Locality

Habitat

Activity

All Time Record

| | | | | | | | | | |
|---|---|---|---|---|---|---|---|---|---|
| | | | | | | | | | |

## 104 Clouded Border *Lomaspilis marginata*

13mm. Dark markings vary in extent, but no other moth has this pattern.

R

| Date & Time | No. |
|---|---|
| | |

Weather

Locality

Habitat

Activity

All Time Record

| | | | | | | | | | | |
|---|---|---|---|---|---|---|---|---|---|---|
| | | | | | | | | | | |

## 105 LATTICED HEATH *Semiothisa clathrata*

14mm. Cream or white, with sooty brown pattern on both surfaces.

R

| Date & Time | No. |
|---|---|
| | |

Weather

Locality

Habitat

All Time Record

| | | | | | | | | | | |
|---|---|---|---|---|---|---|---|---|---|---|

Activity

## 106 SCORCHED WING *Plagodis dolabraria*

18mm. Pattern is unmistakable.

R

| Date & Time | No. |
|---|---|
| | |

Weather

Locality

Habitat

All Time Record

| | | | | | | | | | | |
|---|---|---|---|---|---|---|---|---|---|---|

Activity

### 107 BRIMSTONE MOTH *Opisthograptis luteolata*

22mm. Very variable in size, but pattern is unmistakable.

**R**

**Date & Time**

**No.**

**Weather**

**Locality**

**Habitat**

All Time Record

**Activity**

### 108 SPECKLED YELLOW *Pseudopanthera macularia*

14mm. Day-flying and unmistakable. Bars often broken into separate spots.

**R**

**Date & Time**

**No.**

**Weather**

**Locality**

**Habitat**

All Time Record

**Activity**

## 109 LILAC BEAUTY *Apeira syringaria*

R

19mm. Rests with forewings strangely creased like a dead leaf.

All Time Record

| | | | | | | | | | |
|---|---|---|---|---|---|---|---|---|---|
| | | | | | | | | | |

Date & Time

No.

Weather

Locality

Habitat

Activity

## 110 CANARY-SHOULDERED THORN *Ennomos alniaria*

R

19mm. Bright yellow thorax. Like most thorns, it rests with wings together.

All Time Record

| | | | | | | | | | |
|---|---|---|---|---|---|---|---|---|---|
| | | | | | | | | | |

Date & Time

No.

Weather

Locality

Habitat

Activity

## 111 EARLY THORN *Selenia dentaria*

24mm. Summer brood. Spring insects a little larger and paler.

| R |

**Date & Time**

**No.**

**Weather**

**Locality**

**Habitat**

**All Time Record**

**Activity**

## 112 PURPLE THORN *Selenia tetralunaria*

25mm. Spring brood. Upper surface similar. Summer brood a little browner.

| R |

**Date & Time**

**No.**

**Weather**

**Locality**

**Habitat**

**All Time Record**

**Activity**

## 113 SCALLOPED HAZEL *Odontopera bidentata*

R

24mm. Wings range from cream to dark brown, but margins always scalloped.

| Date & Time | No. |
|---|---|

**Weather**

**Locality**

**Habitat**

**All Time Record**

| | | | | | | | | | |
|---|---|---|---|---|---|---|---|---|---|

**Activity**

## 114 SCALLOPED OAK *Crocallis elinguaria*

R

22mm. Whole forewing may be brownish, and then central bar is indistinct.

| Date & Time | No. |
|---|---|

**Weather**

**Locality**

**Habitat**

**All Time Record**

| | | | | | | | | | |
|---|---|---|---|---|---|---|---|---|---|

**Activity**

## 115 SWALLOWTAILED MOTH *Ourapteryx sambucaria*

R

28mm. An unmistakable moth, with a rather ghostly flight as night falls.

**Date & Time**

**No.**

**Weather**

**Locality**

**Habitat**

**All Time Record**

**Activity**

## 116 FEATHERED THORN *Colotois pennaria*

R

23mm. Male. Female antennae not feathery. Cross-lines often more distinct.

**Date & Time**

**No.**

**Weather**

**Locality**

**Habitat**

**All Time Record**

**Activity**

## 117 ORANGE MOTH  *Angerona prunaria*

R

25mm. Wings often with cream bands or orange or yellow without bands.

**All Time Record**

| | | | | | | | | | | |
|---|---|---|---|---|---|---|---|---|---|---|

| Date & Time | No. |
|---|---|
| | |

**Weather**

**Locality**

**Habitat**

**Activity**

## 118 BRINDLED BEAUTY  *Lycia hirtaria*

R

23mm. Male. Female antennae not feathery. Common in towns.

**All Time Record**

| | | | | | | | | | | |
|---|---|---|---|---|---|---|---|---|---|---|

| Date & Time | No. |
|---|---|
| | |

**Weather**

**Locality**

**Habitat**

**Activity**

## 119 PEPPERED MOTH *Biston betularia*

26mm. Density of speckling varies. Sooty black melanic form common in many areas.

| R |

**Date & Time** | **No.**

**Weather**

**Locality**

**Habitat**

**All Time Record**

**Activity**

## 120 OAK BEAUTY *Biston strataria*

24mm. Like Peppered Moth but forewings browner and normally clearly banded.

| R |

**Date & Time** | **No.**

**Weather**

**Locality**

**Habitat**

**All Time Record**

**Activity**

121 MOTTLED UMBER  *Erannis defoliaria*  [R]

21mm. Male. Forewings often pale with conspicuous dark bands. Female wingless.

**All Time Record**

| | | | | | | | | | |
|---|---|---|---|---|---|---|---|---|---|
| | | | | | | | | | |

**Date & Time**  No.

**Weather**

**Locality**

**Habitat**

**Activity**

122 DOTTED BORDER  *Agriopis marginaria*  [R]

19mm. Like Mottled Umber but with a row of dots round the edge of the hind wing.

**All Time Record**

| | | | | | | | | | |
|---|---|---|---|---|---|---|---|---|---|
| | | | | | | | | | |

**Date & Time**  No.

**Weather**

**Locality**

**Habitat**

**Activity**

**123 WAVED UMBER** *Menophra abruptaria*

19mm. The pattern breaks up the moth's outline, making it hard to see on trees.

R

Date & Time

No.

Weather

Locality

Habitat

All Time Record

Activity

**124 SCALLOPED HOOKTIP** *Falcaria lacertinaria*

18mm. Scalloped wings, with hooked tips, resemble a dead leaf.

R

Date & Time

No.

Weather

Locality

Habitat

All Time Record

Activity

125 PEBBLE HOOKTIP *Drepana falcataria*

18mm. Wings often dirty white with sooty brown markings in Scotland.

R

**Date & Time**

**No.**

**Weather**

**Locality**

**Habitat**

**All Time Record**

**Activity**

126 OAK HOOKTIP *Drepana binaria*

15mm. Sometimes flies by day. Look for the two black dots on the forewing.

R

**Date & Time**

**No.**

**Weather**

**Locality**

**Habitat**

**All Time Record**

**Activity**

## 127 CHINESE CHARACTER *Cilix glaucata*

12mm. At rest, the moth is protected by its resemblance to a bird dropping.

**R**

| Date & Time | No. |
| --- | --- |
| | |

**Weather**

**Locality**

**Habitat**

All Time Record

| | | | | | | | | | |
| --- | --- | --- | --- | --- | --- | --- | --- | --- | --- |

**Activity**

## 128 PEACH BLOSSOM *Thyatiria batis*

19mm. The forewing pattern is unmistakable.

**R**

| Date & Time | No. |
| --- | --- |
| | |

**Weather**

**Locality**

**Habitat**

All Time Record

| | | | | | | | | | |
| --- | --- | --- | --- | --- | --- | --- | --- | --- | --- |

**Activity**

**129** BUFF ARCHES *Habrosyne pyritoides*

20mm. Forewings, held steeply roofwise at rest, have an unmistakable pattern.

| R |

| Date & Time | No. |
| | |

Weather

Locality

Habitat

All Time Record

Activity

**130** DECEMBER MOTH *Poecilocampa populi*

20mm. Quite common on lighted windows on winter evenings.

| R |

| Date & Time | No. |
| | |

Weather

Locality

Habitat

All Time Record

Activity

131 LACKEY *Malacosoma neustria* [R]

19mm. Male. Female larger, with simple antennae. Wings cream to reddish brown.

**Date & Time**

**No.**

**Weather**

**Locality**

**Habitat**

**Activity**

All Time Record

132 OAK EGGAR *Lasiocampa quercus* [R]

40mm. Male. Female is larger and orange, with simple antennae. Male flies by day.

**Date & Time**

**No.**

**Weather**

**Locality**

**Habitat**

**Activity**

All Time Record

133 FOX MOTH *Macrothylacia rubi*

R

30mm. Male. Female is paler, with plain antennae. Male flies by day.

**All Time Record**

| Date & Time | | No. |
| --- | --- | --- |

**Weather**

**Locality**

**Habitat**

**Activity**

134 DRINKER *Euthrix potatoria*

R

30mm. Male. Female larger and straw coloured with plain antennae.

**All Time Record**

**Date & Time** No.

**Weather**

**Locality**

**Habitat**

**Activity**

### 135 LAPPET *Gastropacha quercifolia*

35mm. Resembles a dead leaf when at rest, with hind wing laid flat.

**R**

**Date & Time**

**No.**

**Weather**

**Locality**

**Habitat**

**All Time Record**

**Activity**

### 136 EMPEROR *Saturnia pavonia*

35mm. Female. Male is much browner, with feathery antennae, and flies by day.

**R**

**Date & Time**

**No.**

**Weather**

**Locality**

**Habitat**

**All Time Record**

**Activity**

## 137 KENTISH GLORY *Endromis versicolora* [R]

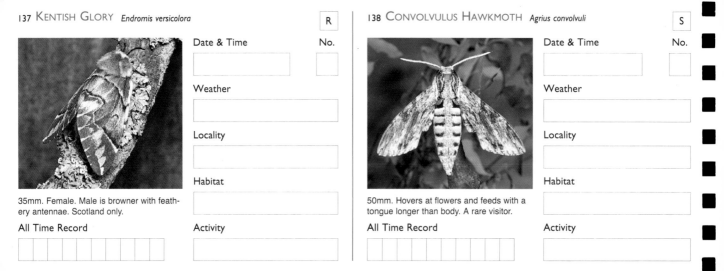

35mm. Female. Male is browner with feathery antennae. Scotland only.

**Date & Time** — **No.**

**Weather**

**Locality**

**Habitat**

**All Time Record**

**Activity**

## 138 CONVOLVULUS HAWKMOTH *Agrius convolvuli* [S]

50mm. Hovers at flowers and feeds with a tongue longer than body. A rare visitor.

**Date & Time** — **No.**

**Weather**

**Locality**

**Habitat**

**All Time Record**

**Activity**

## 139 DEATH'S HEAD HAWKMOTH *Acherontia atropos*

S

60mm. Our largest moth, named for the skull-like pattern on thorax. Rare.

| Date & Time | No. |
|---|---|
| | |

Weather

Locality

Habitat

Activity

All Time Record

| | | | | | | | | | | |
|---|---|---|---|---|---|---|---|---|---|---|

## 140 PRIVET HAWKMOTH *Sphinx ligustri*

R

50mm. Hind wing pinker than Convolvulus Hawkmoth. Our largest resident moth.

| Date & Time | No. |
|---|---|
| | |

Weather

Locality

Habitat

Activity

All Time Record

| | | | | | | | | | | | |
|---|---|---|---|---|---|---|---|---|---|---|---|

## 141 LIME HAWKMOTH *Mimas tiliae*

35mm. Ground colour from pink to olive or reddish brown. Dark band often broken.

R

**Date & Time**

**No.**

**Weather**

**Locality**

**Habitat**

**All Time Record**

**Activity**

## 142 EYED HAWKMOTH *Smerinthus ocellata*

40mm. Frightens enemies by displaying eye-spots when disturbed.

R

**Date & Time**

**No.**

**Weather**

**Locality**

**Habitat**

**All Time Record**

**Activity**

## 143 POPLAR HAWKMOTH *Laothoe populi*

R

40mm. At rest in typical position, with hind wings flat and resembling dead leaves.

| Date & Time | No. |
|---|---|
| | |

Weather

Locality

Habitat

Activity

All Time Record

| | | | | | | | | | | | | |
|---|---|---|---|---|---|---|---|---|---|---|---|---|

## 144 PINE HAWKMOTH *Hyloicus pinastri*

R

35mm. Mating pair, well camouflaged on pine bark.

| Date & Time | No. |
|---|---|
| | |

Weather

Locality

Habitat

Activity

All Time Record

| | | | | | | | | | | | | |
|---|---|---|---|---|---|---|---|---|---|---|---|---|

## 145 BROAD-BORDERED BEE HAWKMOTH *Hemaris fuciformis*

R

24mm. Day-flying and bee-like, usually seen as a brown blur hovering at flowers.

**Date & Time**

**No.**

**Weather**

**Locality**

**Habitat**

All Time Record

**Activity**

## 146 NARROW-BORDERED BEE HAWKMOTH *Hemaris tityus*

R

22mm. Like No. 145 but with narrower margins and blacker belt. Day-flying.

**Date & Time**

**No.**

**Weather**

**Locality**

**Habitat**

All Time Record

**Activity**

### 147 HUMMINGBIRD HAWKMOTH *Macroglossum stellatarum*

S

25mm. Day-flying. Very fast and hovering with a noticeable hum while feeding.

| Date & Time | No. |
|---|---|
| | |

Weather

Locality

Habitat

All Time Record

| | | | | | | | | | | |
|---|---|---|---|---|---|---|---|---|---|---|

Activity

### 148 SPURGE HAWKMOTH *Hyles euphorbiae*

S

33mm. A rare visitor. Like No. 149 but with a narrower and paler front border.

| Date & Time | No. |
|---|---|
| | |

Weather

Locality

Habitat

All Time Record

| | | | | | | | | | | |
|---|---|---|---|---|---|---|---|---|---|---|

Activity

## 149 BEDSTRAW HAWKMOTH *Hyles gallii* [S]

33mm. A sporadic visitor, often missing for several years.

**All Time Record**

| | | | | | | | | | |
|---|---|---|---|---|---|---|---|---|---|

**Date & Time**

**No.**

**Weather**

**Locality**

**Habitat**

**Activity**

## 150 STRIPED HAWKMOTH *Hyles lineata* [S]

40mm. A regular visitor, but only in very small numbers.

**All Time Record**

| | | | | | | | | | |
|---|---|---|---|---|---|---|---|---|---|

**Date & Time**

**No.**

**Weather**

**Locality**

**Habitat**

**Activity**

## 151 ELEPHANT HAWKMOTH *Deilephila elpenor*

R

33mm. Named for caterpillar's trunk-like snout. Look for moth at honeysuckle.

**Date & Time**

**No.**

**Weather**

**Locality**

**Habitat**

**All Time Record**

**Activity**

## 152 SMALL ELEPHANT HAWKMOTH *Deilephila porcellus*

R

25mm. Freshly-emerged, with wings held out to dry. Forewings pink and yellow.

**Date & Time**

**No.**

**Weather**

**Locality**

**Habitat**

**All Time Record**

**Activity**

## 153 BUFF-TIP *Phalera bucephala*

30mm. Buff thorax and wing-tips provide a very efficient twig-like camouflage.

R

Date & Time

No.

Weather

Locality

Habitat

All Time Record

Activity

## 154 PUSS MOTH *Cerura vinula*

35mm. Very furry and with an unmistakable wing pattern.

R

Date & Time

No.

Weather

Locality

Habitat

All Time Record

Activity

## 155 SALLOW KITTEN *Furcula furcula*

R

19mm. Dark central band narrows towards front and has toothed outer margin.

**Date & Time**

**No.**

**Weather**

**Locality**

**Habitat**

**All Time Record**

**Activity**

## 156 LOBSTER MOTH *Stauropus fagi*

R

30mm. Named for the strange, long-legged and vaguely lobster-like caterpillar.

**Date & Time**

**No.**

**Weather**

**Locality**

**Habitat**

**All Time Record**

**Activity**

157 IRON PROMINENT *Notodonta dromedarius*　[R]

Date & Time

No.

Weather

Locality

Habitat

24mm. Like all prominents, it has a prominent tuft of hairs on the forewing.

All Time Record

Activity

158 PEBBLE PROMINENT *Eligmodonta ziczac*　[R]

Date & Time

No.

Weather

Locality

Habitat

24mm. Colour varies, but always with a rounded pebble-like patch near wing-tip.

All Time Record

Activity

## 159 GREAT PROMINENT *Peridea anceps*

R

33mm. Varies from brown to olive green or black. Look for streaks near margin.

| Date & Time | | No. |
|---|---|---|
| | | |

Weather

Locality

Habitat

All Time Record

Activity

## 160 SWALLOW PROMINENT *Pheosia tremula*

R

29mm. At rest in typical position. Very hard to see on tree trunks.

| Date & Time | | No. |
|---|---|---|
| | | |

Weather

Locality

Habitat

All Time Record

Activity

## 161 LESSER SWALLOW PROMINENT *Pheosia gnoma* | R |

26mm. Like No. 160, but has a clear white triangle at rear edge of forewing.

**All Time Record**

| | | | | | | | | | |
|---|---|---|---|---|---|---|---|---|---|

| Date & Time | No. |
|---|---|
| | |

**Weather**

**Locality**

**Habitat**

**Activity**

## 162 COXCOMB PROMINENT *Ptilodon capucina* | R |

23mm. Wings range from pale yellow to purplish brown, but thorax always white.

**All Time Record**

| | | | | | | | | | |
|---|---|---|---|---|---|---|---|---|---|

| Date & Time | No. |
|---|---|
| | |

**Weather**

**Locality**

**Habitat**

**Activity**

## 163 MAPLE PROMINENT *Eligmodonta ziczac*

21mm. Easily identified by the white outer edges of the wings.

R

| Date & Time | No. |
| --- | --- |
| | |

Weather

Locality

Habitat

All Time Record

| | | | | | | | | | | |
| --- | --- | --- | --- | --- | --- | --- | --- | --- | --- | --- |

Activity

## 164 PALE PROMINENT *Pterostoma palpina*

25mm. Resting moth resembles a dead leaf. Long palps at the front.

R

| Date & Time | No. |
| --- | --- |
| | |

Weather

Locality

Habitat

All Time Record

| | | | | | | | | | | |
| --- | --- | --- | --- | --- | --- | --- | --- | --- | --- | --- |

Activity

## 165 SMALL CHOCOLATE-TIP *Clostera pigra*

R

13mm. Forewing sometimes completely brown with a very dark tip.

**Date & Time**

**No.**

**Weather**

**Locality**

**Habitat**

All Time Record

**Activity**

## 166 CHOCOLATE-TIP *Clostera curtula*

R

18mm. Brighter than No. 165, with a more obvious chocolate wing-tip.

**Date & Time**

**No.**

**Weather**

**Locality**

**Habitat**

All Time Record

**Activity**

## 167 LUNAR MARBLED BROWN *Drymonia ruficornis*

21mm. Male. Female has darker wings with a very conspicuous white band.

R

**Date & Time**

**No.**

**Weather**

**Locality**

**Habitat**

All Time Record

**Activity**

## 168 FIGURE-OF-EIGHT *Diloba caeruleocephala*

18mm. Named for the conspicuous double 8 on each forewing.

R

**Date & Time**

**No.**

**Weather**

**Locality**

**Habitat**

All Time Record

**Activity**

## 169 VAPOURER *Orgyia antiqua*

18mm. Male. Day-flying. Female is plump and wingless.

**All Time Record**

| | | | | | | | | | |
|---|---|---|---|---|---|---|---|---|---|
| | | | | | | | | | |

R

**Date & Time**

**No.**

**Weather**

**Locality**

**Habitat**

**Activity**

## 170 PALE TUSSOCK *Calliteara pudibunda*

30mm. Female. Male is smaller and darker. A very hairy moth.

**All Time Record**

| | | | | | | | | | |
|---|---|---|---|---|---|---|---|---|---|
| | | | | | | | | | |

R

**Date & Time**

**No.**

**Weather**

**Locality**

**Habitat**

**Activity**

171 YELLOW-TAIL *Euproctis similis*

20mm. Female. Male has smaller yellow tuft at rear.

R

| Date & Time | No. |
| | |

Weather

Locality

Habitat

All Time Record

Activity

172 BLACK ARCHES *Lymantria monacha*

24mm. Male. Female less densely marked but otherwise similar.

R

| Date & Time | No. |
| | |

Weather

Locality

Habitat

All Time Record

Activity

173 ROSY FOOTMAN *Miltochrista miniata*

R

14mm. Pattern and colour are unmistakable.

All Time Record

| | | | | | | | | | | |
|---|---|---|---|---|---|---|---|---|---|---|

Date & Time

No.

Weather

Locality

Habitat

Activity

174 WOOD TIGER *Parasemia plantaginis*

R

18mm. Pale areas are either yellow or white. Male flies by day.

All Time Record

| | | | | | | | | | | |
|---|---|---|---|---|---|---|---|---|---|---|

Date & Time

No.

Weather

Locality

Habitat

Activity

## 175 GARDEN TIGER *Arctia caja*

35mm. Forewing pattern varies. Hind wing may be yellow instead of orange.

R

| Date & Time | No. |
| --- | --- |
| | |

Weather

Locality

Habitat

All Time Record

| | | | | | | | | | | | |
| --- | --- | --- | --- | --- | --- | --- | --- | --- | --- | --- | --- |

Activity

## 176 CREAM-SPOT TIGER *Arctia villica*

30mm. As in all tiger moths, bright colours warn of an unpleasant taste.

R

| Date & Time | No. |
| --- | --- |
| | |

Weather

Locality

Habitat

All Time Record

| | | | | | | | | | | | |
| --- | --- | --- | --- | --- | --- | --- | --- | --- | --- | --- | --- |

Activity

## 177 CLOUDED BUFF *Diacrisia sannio*

R

22mm. Male. Smaller female is largely orange. Male often flies by day.

**Date & Time**

**No.**

**Weather**

**Locality**

**Habitat**

**All Time Record**

**Activity**

## 178 SCARLET TIGER *Callimorpha dominula*

R

27mm. Size of white spots varies. Day-flying. Becoming rare in many areas.

**Date & Time**

**No.**

**Weather**

**Locality**

**Habitat**

**All Time Record**

**Activity**

## 179 RUBY TIGER *Phragmatobia fuliginosa*

17mm. Hind wing sometimes largely black. Often flies by day.

R

**Date & Time**

**No.**

**Weather**

**Locality**

**Habitat**

**All Time Record**

**Activity**

## 180 WHITE ERMINE *Spilosoma lubricipeda*

20mm. Black spots vary in number and size. Abdomen largely yellow.

R

**Date & Time**

**No.**

**Weather**

**Locality**

**Habitat**

**All Time Record**

**Activity**

## 181 BUFF ERMINE *Spilosoma lutea*

19mm. Male. Female is paler and has plain antennae.

R

**Date & Time**

**No.**

**Weather**

**Locality**

**Habitat**

**All Time Record**

**Activity**

## 182 MUSLIN ERMINE *Diaphora mendica*

17mm. Male. Female is like White Ermine but thinly scaled and with white abdomen.

R

**Date & Time**

**No.**

**Weather**

**Locality**

**Habitat**

**All Time Record**

**Activity**

183 CINNABAR *Tyria jacobaeae*

19mm. An unmistakable moth, often fluttering weakly by day when disturbed.

R

Date & Time

No.

Weather

Locality

Habitat

All Time Record

Activity

184 HEART & DART *Agrotis exclamationis*

19mm. Named for the shape of the dark wing marks. Wings held flat at rest.

R

Date & Time

No.

Weather

Locality

Habitat

All Time Record

Activity

185 FLAME MOTH *Axylia putris*

16mm. Wings wrapped around body at rest.

R

**Date & Time**

**No.**

**Weather**

**Locality**

**Habitat**

**All Time Record**

**Activity**

186 FLAME SHOULDER *Ochropleura plecta*

15mm. Wings held flat at rest. Hind wings very white.

R

**Date & Time**

**No.**

**Weather**

**Locality**

**Habitat**

**All Time Record**

**Activity**

## 187 BROAD-BORDERED YELLOW UNDERWING *Noctua fimbriata* [R]

26mm. Female. Male is darker. Hind wing yellow with broad black border.

**Date & Time**

**No.**

**Weather**

**Locality**

**Habitat**

All Time Record

**Activity**

## 188 LARGE YELLOW UNDERWING *Noctua pronuba* [R]

27mm. Male. Female forewing is pale brown. Wings held flat at rest.

**Date & Time**

**No.**

**Weather**

**Locality**

**Habitat**

All Time Record

**Activity**

189 AUTUMNAL RUSTIC *Paradiarsia glareosa* | R |

Date & Time

No.

Weather

Locality

Habitat

17mm. Forewings range from pale grey to pinkish brown. Hind wings very white.

All Time Record

Activity

190 SETACEOUS HEBREW CHARACTER *Xestia c-nigrum* | R |

Date & Time

No.

Weather

Locality

Habitat

20mm. One of our commonest moths. Wings held flat at rest. Hind wings white.

All Time Record

Activity

191 DOT MOTH *Melanchra persicariae*

22mm. Rests with wings roofwise over body. Very common in gardens.

R

| Date & Time | No. |
| --- | --- |
|  |  |

Weather

Locality

Habitat

All Time Record

| | | | | | | | | | | |
| --- | --- | --- | --- | --- | --- | --- | --- | --- | --- | --- |

Activity

192 LIGHT BROCADE *Lacanobia w-latinum*

21mm. Look for the white patch and dark flash at the base of the forewing.

R

| Date & Time | No. |
| --- | --- |
|  |  |

Weather

Locality

Habitat

All Time Record

| | | | | | | | | | | |
| --- | --- | --- | --- | --- | --- | --- | --- | --- | --- | --- |

Activity

## 193 BRIGHT-LINE BROWN-EYE *Lacanobia oleracea*

R

20mm. Forewing colour ranges from pale reddish brown to very dark brown.

**All Time Record**

| | | | | | | | | | |
|---|---|---|---|---|---|---|---|---|---|
| | | | | | | | | | |

**Date & Time**

**No.**

**Weather**

**Locality**

**Habitat**

**Activity**

## 194 BROOM MOTH *Ceramica pisi*

R

19mm. Forewing varies from pale to deep brown; wavy cream line always present.

**All Time Record**

| | | | | | | | | | |
|---|---|---|---|---|---|---|---|---|---|
| | | | | | | | | | |

**Date & Time**

**No.**

**Weather**

**Locality**

**Habitat**

**Activity**

## 195 BROAD-BARRED WHITE *Hecatera bicolorata*

15mm. Ground colour of forewing ranges from white to bluish-grey.

R

| Date & Time | No. |
| --- | --- |
|  |  |

Weather

Locality

Habitat

All Time Record

| | | | | | | | | | | |
| --- | --- | --- | --- | --- | --- | --- | --- | --- | --- | --- |

Activity

## 196 VARIED CORONET *Hadena compta*

15mm. White cross-bar always complete. Common in gardens.

R

| Date & Time | No. |
| --- | --- |
|  |  |

Weather

Locality

Habitat

All Time Record

| | | | | | | | | | | |
| --- | --- | --- | --- | --- | --- | --- | --- | --- | --- | --- |

Activity

## 197 ANTLER MOTH  *Cerapteryx graminis*

16mm. Antler-like markings vary in intensity. Female is larger than male.

R

Date & Time

No.

Weather

Locality

Habitat

All Time Record

Activity

## 198 HEBREW CHARACTER  *Orthosia gothica*

17mm. Like No. 190 but rests with wings roofwise. Hind wings are brown.

R

Date & Time

No.

Weather

Locality

Habitat

All Time Record

Activity

## 199 BROWN-LINE BRIGHT-EYE *Mythimna conigera* | R |

17mm. Ground colour varies from yellowish brown to a rich orange-brown.

**Date & Time** | **No.**

**Weather**

**Locality**

**Habitat**

**All Time Record**

**Activity**

## 200 SMOKY WAINSCOT *Mythimna impura* | R |

17mm. Always a dark line through centre of forewing. Hind wing smoky brown.

**Date & Time** | **No.**

**Weather**

**Locality**

**Habitat**

**All Time Record**

**Activity**

## 201 MULLEIN MOTH  *Cucullia verbasci*

R

24mm. Like a piece of bark when resting.
Caterpillars destroy garden mulleins.

**Date & Time**

**No.**

**Weather**

**Locality**

**Habitat**

All Time Record

**Activity**

## 202 SPRAWLER  *Brachionycha sphinx*

R

20mm. Forewing ranges from grey to reddish brown.

**Date & Time**

**No.**

**Weather**

**Locality**

**Habitat**

All Time Record

**Activity**

## 203 GREEN-BRINDLED CRESCENT *Allophyes oxyacanthae*

21mm. The typical form. Often sooty brown, but white flash always visible.

R

**Date & Time**

**No.**

**Weather**

**Locality**

**Habitat**

All Time Record

**Activity**

## 204 MERVEILLE DU JOUR *Dichonia aprilina*

23mm. Well camouflaged among tree-trunk lichens. Green fades with age.

R

**Date & Time**

**No.**

**Weather**

**Locality**

**Habitat**

All Time Record

**Activity**

## 205 FLAME BROCADE  *Trigonophora flammea*

24mm. A sporadic visitor, mainly in autumn. Fond of ivy blossom.

S

**Date & Time**

**No.**

**Weather**

**Locality**

**Habitat**

All Time Record

**Activity**

## 206 ORANGE SALLOW  *Xanthia citrago*

17mm. A common visitor to lighted windows in late summer.

R

**Date & Time**

**No.**

**Weather**

**Locality**

**Habitat**

All Time Record

**Activity**

## 207 BARRED SALLOW *Xanthia aurago*

R

16mm. Central band ranges from primrose yellow to deep orange.

**All Time Record**

| | | | | | | | | | | |
|---|---|---|---|---|---|---|---|---|---|---|

**Date & Time**

No.

**Weather**

**Locality**

**Habitat**

**Activity**

## 208 PINK-BARRED SALLOW *Xanthia togata*

R

16mm. Common at lights in autumn. Look for the purple head and collar.

**All Time Record**

| | | | | | | | | | | |
|---|---|---|---|---|---|---|---|---|---|---|

**Date & Time**

No.

**Weather**

**Locality**

**Habitat**

**Activity**

209 SALLOW *Xanthia icteritia*

17mm. Yellow or orange with variable dark markings. Head and collar yellow.

R

Date & Time

No.

Weather

Locality

Habitat

All Time Record

Activity

210 GREY DAGGER *Acronicta psi*

19mm. Pale to dark grey, with black dagger-shaped marks.

R

Date & Time

No.

Weather

Locality

Habitat

All Time Record

Activity

211 OLD LADY *Mormo maura*

34mm. Named for the pattern, reminiscent of the cloaks of elderly ladies.

R

| Date & Time | No. |
| --- | --- |
| | |

Weather

Locality

Habitat

All Time Record

| | | | | | | | | | |
| --- | --- | --- | --- | --- | --- | --- | --- | --- | --- |

Activity

212 ANGLE SHADES *Phlogophora meticulosa*

24mm. In typical resting position, with wings crumpled like a dead leaf.

R

| Date & Time | No. |
| --- | --- |
| | |

Weather

Locality

Habitat

All Time Record

| | | | | | | | | | |
| --- | --- | --- | --- | --- | --- | --- | --- | --- | --- |

Activity

### 213 STRAW UNDERWING *Thalpophila matura*

R

21mm. Forewing often dark with pattern obscured, but white streak remains.

| Date & Time | No. |
|---|---|
|  |  |

**Weather**

**Locality**

**Habitat**

**All Time Record**

| | | | | | | | | | |
|---|---|---|---|---|---|---|---|---|---|

**Activity**

### 214 WHITE-SPOTTED PINION *Cosmia diffinis*

R

16mm. Easily recognised by the white spots.

| Date & Time | No. |
|---|---|
|  |  |

**Weather**

**Locality**

**Habitat**

**All Time Record**

| | | | | | | | | | |
|---|---|---|---|---|---|---|---|---|---|

**Activity**

## 215 FROSTED ORANGE *Gortyna flavago*

R

19mm. Outer wing margin may be orange. Caterpillars can be potato pests.

**Date & Time**

**No.**

**Weather**

**Locality**

**Habitat**

**All Time Record**

**Activity**

## 216 GREEN SILVER-LINES *Pseudoips fagana*

R

17mm. Hind wing yellowish in male, white in female. May be only two cross lines.

**Date & Time**

**No.**

**Weather**

**Locality**

**Habitat**

**All Time Record**

**Activity**

### 217 NUT-TREE TUSSOCK *Colocasia coryli*

R

17mm. Outer part of forewing ranges from greyish white to smoky brown.

| Date & Time | No. |
| --- | --- |
| | |

**Weather**

**Locality**

**Habitat**

All Time Record

Activity

### 218 GOLDEN PLUSIA *Polychrisia moneta*

R

20mm. A common garden insect. The caterpillars damage delphiniums.

| Date & Time | No. |
| --- | --- |
| | |

**Weather**

**Locality**

**Habitat**

All Time Record

Activity

219 BURNISHED BRASS *Diachrisia chrysitis*

R

19mm. Forewing golden or metallic green, often crossed by a brown bar.

All Time Record

| | | | | | | | | | |
|--|--|--|--|--|--|--|--|--|--|
| | | | | | | | | | |

Date & Time

No.

Weather

Locality

Habitat

Activity

---

220 GOLD SPOT *Plusia festucae*

R

20mm. Ground colour varies from golden yellow to brown.

All Time Record

| | | | | | | | | | | | |
|--|--|--|--|--|--|--|--|--|--|--|--|
| | | | | | | | | | | | |

Date & Time

No.

Weather

Locality

Habitat

Activity

## 221 SILVER-Y *Autographa gamma*

20mm. Named for the silvery Y-shaped mark. Very common, often flying by day.

**S**

**Date & Time**

**No.**

**Weather**

**Locality**

**Habitat**

**Activity**

All Time Record

## 222 BEAUTIFUL GOLDEN Y *Autographa pulchrina*

20mm. Look for the silver-edged kidney-shaped mark beyond the Y.

**R**

**Date & Time**

**No.**

**Weather**

**Locality**

**Habitat**

**Activity**

All Time Record

## 223 PLAIN GOLDEN Y *Autographa jota*

20mm. No kidney-shaped mark beyond the
Y, which sits on a plain brown rectangle.

All Time Record

| | | | | | | | | | | |
|---|---|---|---|---|---|---|---|---|---|---|

R

| Date & Time | No. |
|---|---|
| | |

Weather

Locality

Habitat

Activity

## 224 SPECTACLE *Abrostola triplasia*

17mm. Named for the pale circles, like a
pair of spectacles, at front of thorax.

All Time Record

| | | | | | | | | | | |
|---|---|---|---|---|---|---|---|---|---|---|

R

| Date & Time | No. |
|---|---|
| | |

Weather

Locality

Habitat

Activity

## 225 RED UNDERWING *Catocala nupta*

40mm. Very difficult to see on tree trunks when wings are closed.

All Time Record

R

| | | | | | | | | | | |
|---|---|---|---|---|---|---|---|---|---|---|

Date & Time

No.

Weather

Locality

Habitat

Activity

## 226 MOTHER SHIPTON *Callistege mi*

15mm. Day-flying. Look for the witch-like profile on each forewing.

All Time Record

R

| | | | | | | | | | | |
|---|---|---|---|---|---|---|---|---|---|---|

Date & Time

No.

Weather

Locality

Habitat

Activity

### 227 HERALD *Scoliopteryx libatrix*

22mm. Hibernates as adult, often hanging upside-down and looking like a dead leaf.

R

**Date & Time**

**No.**

**Weather**

**Locality**

**Habitat**

**All Time Record**

**Activity**

### 228 BEAUTIFUL HOOKTIP *Laspeyria flexula*

15mm. The amount of purple varies. Leaf-like form provides excellent camouflage.

R

**Date & Time**

**No.**

**Weather**

**Locality**

**Habitat**

**All Time Record**

**Activity**

# INDEX

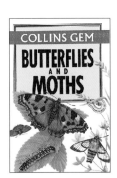

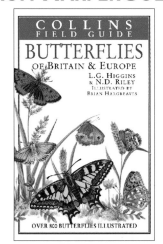
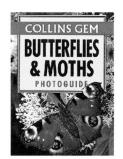

# TIME TO ORDER YOUR NEW COLLINS CHECKBOOK

Please send me ☐ copies of Collins Checkbook of British Butterflies and Moths @ £4.99

Please send me ☐ copies of Collins Checkbook of British Birds @ £4.99

Please send me ☐ copies of Collins Checkbook of British Wildflowers @ £4.99

Please send me ☐ copies of Collins Checkbook of British Trees @ £4.99

*Postage and Packing is FREE*

Subtotal £............

I enclose a cheque made payable to HarperCollins*Publishers* for £......................

Or Please debit my Access*/Visa* card for £......................
*(delete as necessary)

Credit Card No. ............................................ Expiry Date ........................

Name _____

Address _____

_____

Postcode

Signature _____

Please send your order to HarperCollins*Publishers*, Dept 205E, Westerhill Road, Bishopbriggs, Glasgow, G64 2QT. Or ring the **24-HOUR CREDIT CARD HOTLINE** on 041 772 2281 Glasgow or 081 307 4052 London (Access & Visa only please)

# BOOKS AVAILABLE IN THIS SERIES